GARFIELD
SCARED SILLY

By Jim "Voodoo" Davis

with Ghostly Gagwriters
Mark "The Dark" Acey & Scott "Blood Clot" Nickel
Designed by Kenny "Cool Ghoul" Goetzinger

A Ballantine Book
Published by The Ballantine Publishing Group
Copyright © 2001 by PAWS, Incorporated. All rights reserved.

www.ballantinebooks.com

ISBN 0-345-44921-5

Manufactured in the United States of America

First Edition: July 2001

10 9 8 7 6 5 4 3

GARFIELD'S TOP TEN NIGHTMARES

10. **Nermal gets cloned**

9. **Vet prescribes "chain saw therapy"**

8. **Falls into vat of Odie drool**

7. **Fleas vote him "Most Bloodsuckable"**

6. **Inhales next to Jon's dirty socks**

5. **Forced to watch the "All Lassie" channel**

4. **Trapped for a week inside health food store**

3. **Cat fur the latest thing for women's coats**

2. **Meets huge spider with an attitude**

1. **Diet Monday!**

MONSTER MADNESS

What would you get if you crossed
a man-made monster with a pig?
Frankenswine!

How do you get Frankenstein
up in the morning?
Jumper cables!

What did Frankenstein tell his bride?
"We were made for each other!"

COME TO MUMMY

Why did everyone run from the Mummy?
Because it had been four thousand
years since he took a bath!

What happened when
the Mummy was bad?
He got sent to his tomb!

Why did the Mummy steal
the rolls of toilet paper?
He needed a new wardrobe!

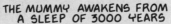

CREEEEEEEK

THE MUMMY AWAKENS FROM A SLEEP OF 3000 YEARS

AND SETS HIS SNOOZE ALARM FOR ANOTHER CENTURY

JIM DAVIS 7-20

BOY, AM I STARVED

JIM DAVIS 7-21

I WONDER WHAT MUMMIES EAT?

CREEPY

FRANKENFURTER

GARZILLA

THIS COULD BE ANY REFRIGERATOR, MAYBE YOURS

DEEP WITHIN THE FROZEN WASTES IT LURKS

© 1987 PAWS, INC. All Rights Reserved.

ANCIENT MAYONNAISE, FOSSILIZED CABBAGE, SLOWLY MUTATING OVER UNTOLD EONS, GRADUALLY ACHIEVING CONSCIOUSNESS...

UNTIL THAT TERRIBLE DAY WHEN IT IS UNLEASHED UPON AN UNSUSPECTING WORLD

THE COLESLAW THAT TIME FORGOT!
AYIEEE!
JIM DAVIS 7-19

CUTE, GARFIELD. NOW FINISH CLEANING OUT THE REFRIGERATOR

QUIET, FOOL! YOU'LL AWAKEN THE SLEEPING SPUDS FROM THE PLANET FUNGUS

STRANGE

GARFIELD IS SO LAZY, HE ONCE HAD HIS COFFEE INTRAVENOUSLY!

ODIE MOONLIGHTS AS A CHIA PET!

BUT WEIRD!

GARFIELD ONCE SWALLOWED AN ENTIRE MAILMAN!

B·U·U·R·R·R·RP!

GARFIELD ONCE UNCORKED A BURP THAT REGISTERED 6.2 ON THE RICHTER SCALE!

KILLER KNOCK-

Knock, knock!
Who's there?
Juana.
Juana who?
Juana go see a scary movie?

Knock, knock!
Who's there?
Ivan.
Ivan who?
Ivan to bite your neck!

Knock, knock!
Who's there?
Harry.
Harry who?
Harry and open the door
before the monster gets me!

KNOCKS

Knock, knock!
Who's there?
Matt.
Matt who?
Matt scientist! Can I interest
you in a brain transplant?

Knock, knock!
Who's there?
Frank.
Frank who?
Frank N. Stein!

Knock, knock!
Who's there?
Yvonne.
Yvonne who?
Yvonne to vatch "Buffy the Vampire Slayer"!

FANGTASTIC FUNNIES

What did the vampire tell his dentist?
   "Fangs for the checkup!"

Why did the vampire go to
the fast-food restaurant?
He wanted a quick bite!

Why does Dracula wear a tuxedo?
Because he'd look silly in an evening gown!

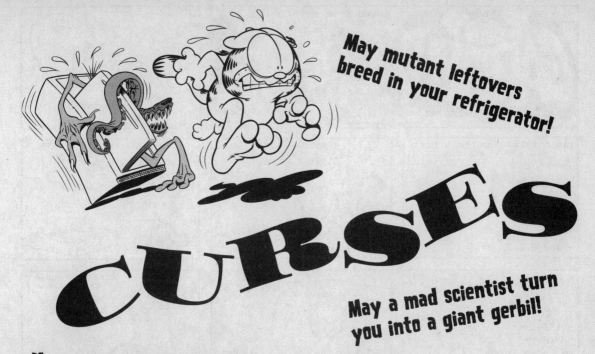

DO YOU EXPECT ME TO BE SEEN IN PUBLIC WITH YOU DRESSED LIKE THAT?

CLICK

WHY DO I STAY UP AND WATCH THOSE OLD HORROR MOVIES?

WHAT IF THERE'S A MONSTER UNDER MY BED?

THAT'S SILLY. A MONSTER COULDN'T FIT UNDER THERE

UNLESS OF COURSE, IT'S A REAL THIN MONSTER

THE SUN SHOULD BE UP SOON

GHOSTLY GIGGLES

What would you get if you crossed
a ghost with Garfield's teddy bear?
Spooky Pooky!

Why should ghosts never tell lies?
**Because people can see
right through them!**

What do spooks eat for dinner?
Ghost beef.

THE GHOST CREPT CLOSER AND CLOSER....

SUDDENLY, IT... GRABBED HIM!

AIEEE!

THAT PART ALWAYS SCARES HIM

www.garfield.com

JIM DAVIS 5-20

BOO

HUH?

BOO

OH... RIGHT

NOT THE SCARIEST GHOST MOVIE I'VE EVER SEEN

10-30

JIM DAVIS

HEY, GARFIELD, CHECK OUT MY GHOST COSTUME

VERY NICE

JIM DAVIS 10-27

UH-HUH...

HOW CUTE

Hysterical Howlers

Why did the little werewolf
stay home from school?
It was a howliday!

Which side of a werewolf
has the most fur?
The outside!

Why was the werewolf too
embarrassed to go out of the house?
He was having a bad fur day.

TOP TEN SIGNS THAT SOMEONE IS A WEREWOLF

10. You catch him sniffing your dog

9. If you even mention a full moon, he salivates to beat the band!

8. He can open a can of soup with his finger

7. He owns a silver-bulletproof vest

6. It takes him five-and-a-half hours to shave

5. You compliment him on his fur jacket, and he's not wearing one

4. He can't pass a graveyard without stopping to maul the old gravedigger

3. He excuses himself to go to the "Wolfmen's Room"

2. He has ring around the flea collar

1. You smell victim on his breath!

TAP
TAP

EEEK!

JIM DAVIS 10-30

OH, C'MON... THAT'S NOT SCARY

NOW, THAT'S SCARY

JIM DAVIS 11-1

GARFIELD'S TOP TEN LEAST FAVORITE HALLOWEEN COSTUMES

10. Snoopy

9. A raisin

8. An alarm clock

7. A belly dancer

6. A sumo wrestler

5. A fire hydrant

4. A giant chew bone

3. Jar Jar Binks

2. The Creature from the Porta Potti

1. Jon Arbuckle

What do hungry witches do
when they want fast food?
They use the fly-through window!

What do witches put on their hair?
Scare spray!

Why did the young girl want to be a sorceress?
So she could grow up to be witch and famous.

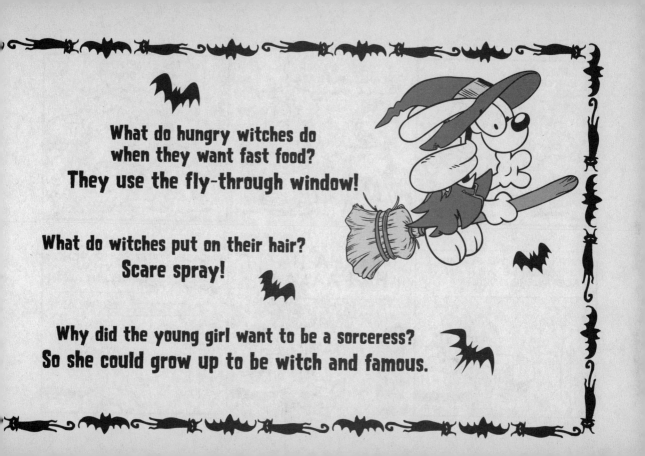

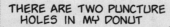

GARFIELD, I THINK WE HAVE VAMPIRES

THERE ARE TWO PUNCTURE HOLES IN MY DONUT

AND ALL THE JELLY'S BEEN SUCKED OUT!

I'LL BE IN MY COFFIN

"...AND WHILE THE DOG SLEPT, THE CAT SAT AT THE WHETSTONE SHARPENING HIS CLAWS."

BED TIME STORIES

"TONIGHT WOULD BE AN EVENTFUL NIGHT INDEED..." TO BE CONTINUED...

BED TIME STORIES

JIM DAVIS 3-14

In a Perfect World...

horror movies would be REALLY scary!

GARFIELD'S CHAMBER OF HORRORS

The Vampire   **The Mummy**   **The Werewolf**   **The Telemarketer**

FRIGHT GAGS

What would you get if you crossed
Garfield with a teen horror film?
I Know What You Ate Last Summer!

What would you get if you crossed
October 31st with a hot dog?
Halloweiner!

What flavor of ice cream do monsters like best?
Cookies and Scream!

GRAVE RAVES

Did you hear about the teenage zombie movie?
It's called *Night of the Living Dude!*

What did the zombie eat for dinner?
A seven-corpse meal!

What machine smoothes the ice at
undead skating rinks?
The Zomboni!

POKE POKE

© 1997 PAWS, INC. All Rights Reserved.

POKE POKE

JIM DAVIS 10-26

Your face is so gross, you make Frankenstein look like Brad Pitt!

You're no ordinary geek. You're Geekzilla!

If space aliens captured you, they'd report no intelligent life on Earth!

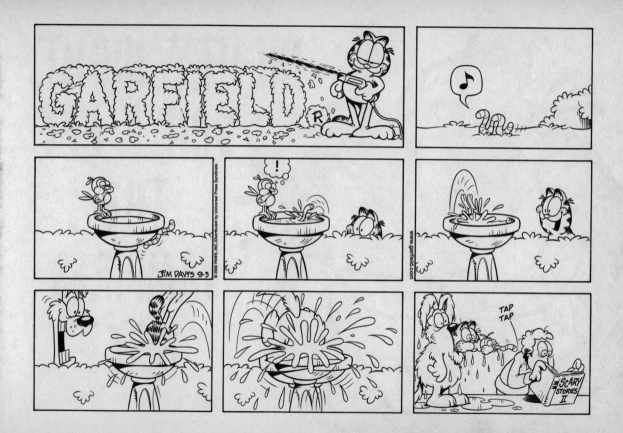